# EXCALIBUR

by Chris Buckton

Illustrated by Alan Down

# CAST

**Gryflet**
a young squire

**Merlin**
a magician

**Arthur**
King of England

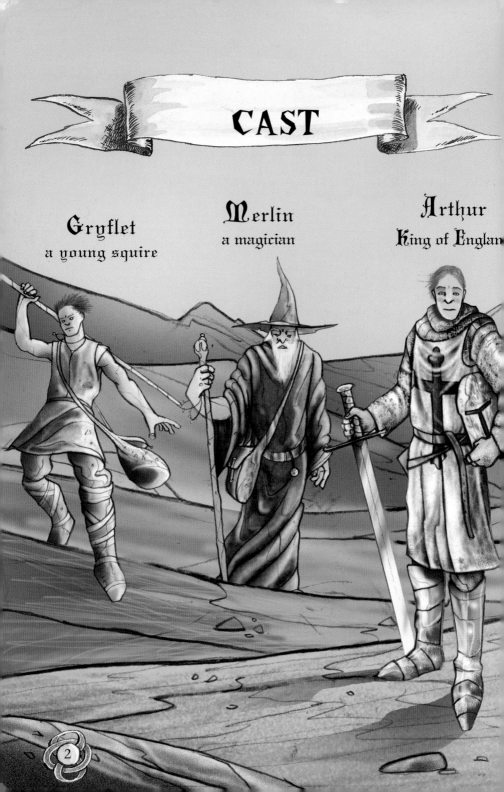

Sir Pellinore
a rebel knight

Narrator

Lady
of the Lake

3

**Narrator**   *Young Arthur has drawn Merlin's magic sword from the stone, and proved himself the true King of England. When he was crowned, he made a solemn vow to bring peace to his kingdom. He gathered his most loyal knights together at his court in Camelot and drove out invaders, but still there is unrest. Many strong barons want power for themselves. And a rebel knight, Sir Pellinore, is murdering innocent travellers …*

# SCENE ONE

*The courtyard outside the castle at Camelot. Arthur and his servants are getting ready to go hunting. Enter Gryflet on horseback, leading another horse with a body slumped across its saddle.*

**Gryflet** *(desperate)* Vengeance! Give me vengeance!

**Arthur** Whose body is this? Who has committed this deed?

**Gryflet** It is my master, Sir Miles, as goodly a knight as any in the land. Slain by the wicked Sir Pellinore.

**Arthur** A name to tremble at! Sir Pellinore has caused us much trouble.

**Gryflet** He has set his tent on the road not far from here. He lies in wait for any who pass, and challenges them to joust with him. He murdered my master for no reason. We were on our way to join King Arthur.

**Arthur** I am the Arthur you seek. A sad welcome to Camelot!

*Gryflet dismounts and kneels before Arthur.*

**Gryflet**   My noble King, make me a knight so that I may avenge my master's death. Let me challenge Sir Pellinore, I beg you.

**Arthur**   Squire Gryflet, you are too inexperienced for such a battle. Pellinore is the strongest knight in the world. Even I would hesitate …

**Gryflet**   *(leaps up, excited)* My anger will give me strength beyond my years. I pray you, make me a knight, and give me arms, so that I can ride out to serve your court.

**Arthur**   I like your spirit. You are a brave youth. *(Pauses, then continues reluctantly)* Very well. Kneel, Gryflet, and I will grant your wish. But you must agree to ride against him only once. If you are unhorsed, you must promise to return here straight away.

**Gryflet**   *(eagerly)* My lord, I promise!

*Gryflet kneels. Arthur knights him.*

**Arthur**   Arise, Sir Gryflet. My blessings go with you. Remember your promise! We will wait for you here.

**Narrator**   *The good knight Gryflet does keep his promise. But he returns all too soon …*

*Enter Gryflet on horseback, clinging to the saddle.*

**Arthur**   Alas! It is what I feared – Sir Gryflet is sore wounded!

**Gryflet**   *(bravely but faintly)* You were right, noble sire, Sir Pellinore is too strong for me. His lance has pierced me in the side … But I kept my promise …

*Sir Gryflet faints and begins to fall from his horse. Arthur catches him.*

**Arthur**   Men, assist him into the castle and tend his wounds. I have a score to settle. I will keep my identity secret, and teach Sir Pellinore a lesson.

*Arthur closes the visor on his helmet and spurs his horse out of the castle yard.*

# SCENE TWO

*The forest near Camelot*

**Narrator** *Arthur rides hard into the forest to take revenge on Sir Pellinore. But on his way he comes across three robbers attacking an old man. Arthur cannot pass by and leave a defenceless man in trouble. He draws his sword and rides furiously at the robbers. They bolt into the forest.*

**Arthur** *(helping the old man to his feet)* Now then, my good old man … *(He recognises the old man's face)* Why – Merlin! *(Boastfully)* It's lucky I was here to save you, or you would have been food for worms!

**Merlin** *(quietly)* Not so, Arthur. I could have saved myself if I had wanted to. It is you who draws near to death, not I. Your anger leads you into danger.

**Narrator** *But Arthur pays no heed to Merlin's warning. He rides on until he reaches Sir Pellinore's tent. The knight is waiting, fully armed, on his great warhorse, blocking the path.*

**Arthur** Sir Knight! Why do you threaten all who pass this way?

**Pellinore** *(tersely)* I do what I please and how I please. No man can deter me.

**Arthur** *(challenging)* Move over or you will pay with your life!

**Pellinore** *(laughing arrogantly)* Ha! It is you who must pay! You must joust with me before you can pass.

**Arthur** *(angrily, levelling his lance)* Come then. I will make you sorry you blocked my path!

**Narrator**  *Sir Pellinore and King Arthur spur their horses and thunder towards each other. They joust together until their lances are shattered. Sir Pellinore strikes King Arthur's shield so hard that horse and man fall to the ground.*

**Arthur**  *(defiantly seizing his sword)* I am not defeated yet. Dismount and fight on foot!

**Pellinore**  I am an honourable knight. I will not take advantage of your helplessness.

**Narrator**  *And so Sir Pellinore climbs down from his horse and takes up his sword. Then begins a fierce battle. They hack and hew at each other until their armour is dented and their shields buckled. They are well-matched fighters. Both men are wounded, but neither will yield. Then, as King Arthur blocks Sir Pellinore's furious strokes, his sword breaks in two.*

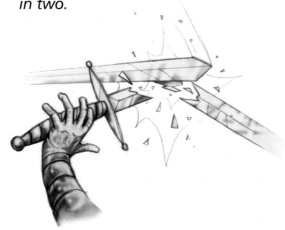

**Pellinore** *(triumphantly)* Now you are in my power! Surrender or die!

**Arthur** *(fiercely)* I will never surrender! I would rather die!

**Pellinore** Then die you shall! *(Raises his sword to cut off Arthur's head)*

**Merlin** Hold, Sir Pellinore! Do you know who it is you would kill? This is Arthur, your King. Destroy him, and you will destroy all hope for a united Britain.

**Pellinore** *(shocked)* My King … Forgive me.

**Merlin** *(touching Sir Pellinore gently on the head)* Sleep now … and forget …

*Sir Pellinore sinks to the ground in a deep trance.*

**Arthur**  *(weakly)* Merlin! You have saved my life … I could not have fought for a moment longer … I met my match in Pellinore.

**Merlin**  It is no bad thing to learn such a lesson. Even the great King Arthur can be defeated! You were lucky that I was here to protect you.

**Arthur**  Do not kill him, Merlin. He is a brave and mighty knight.

**Merlin**  Fear not. He will wake again soon. I can foretell that he and his sons will serve you loyally. You will need good fighters to help you rule your kingdom.

**Arthur**  *(despairingly)* But the sword that made me King is broken. I am useless!

**Merlin**  That sword has served its purpose. Your own sword, Excalibur, awaits you. But first you must rest so that your wounds can heal.

# SCENE THREE

*On the shore of Lake Avalon*

**Narrator** *Arthur rests for three days with Merlin in a hermit's cave deep in the forest. When his wounds are healed, they ride together until they come to a beautiful lake, half hidden in mist. Its clear blue water reflects the dark, mysterious mountains which surround it.*

**Arthur** What is this place?

**Merlin** This is the lake that separates life from death. Beyond the mist lies Avalon, the land of the living dead, where the great heroes wait until their re-awakening. Avalon, the land that you and I will go to when our time is come.

**Arthur** But why are we here now?

**Merlin** Be still, and attend carefully … Behold, there, in the centre of the lake. What do you see?

**Arthur**    *(peering into the mist)* There's a rock …
no, maybe a bird … no – an arm! A ghostly
arm … with a white silk sleeve, and it's
holding … *(Whispers)* It's holding a
weapon! A wondrous sword, with a golden
hilt … and a jewelled scabbard! Is it a
dream? Is it real?

**Merlin**    *(quietly)* There is strong magic in this place.
The arm that you see is from another
world, but the sword it holds is real
enough. It is Excalibur.

**Arthur**    *(awed)* Excalibur!

**Merlin**    None may stand against its stroke. I have
led you to your sword. And look, the Lady
of the Lake, who has woven this spell.
She comes to greet you. Go down and
meet her.

**Narrator**    *Out of the mists comes a beautiful damsel
dressed in white silk with a golden girdle.
She walks gracefully across the water until
she stands before Arthur on the shore.*

**Lady**  I am the Lady of the Lake. I have been expecting you. I come to tell you that your sword awaits you yonder. Its name is Excalibur, which means 'cut steel'. It was forged by elven folk in Avalon, and is intended for you alone.

**Arthur**  But how shall I reach it?

**Lady**  You will take my boat and claim what is yours.

**Narrator**  *So Arthur follows the Lady to where a small boat lies hidden in the reeds. When Arthur steps in, the boat floats across the lake as if it is pulled by unseen hands. As he reaches the centre of the lake, Arthur sees the phantom arm stretch out towards him. His heart beating, he leans out of the boat and takes the sword with its scabbard. The arm sinks slowly out of sight beneath the misty waters. Then the boat carries Arthur back to the shore with his precious gift.*

**Arthur**  (*proudly, brandishing the sword*) It is truly a marvellous weapon! It fits my hand perfectly. Even Pellinore couldn't break this sword!

**Lady**  Excalibur will serve you well. Accept it humbly, and draw it only to defend what is right.

**Arthur**  I swear that I will use it wisely and well.

**Lady**  Which do you value more, the sword or its scabbard?

**Arthur**  Oh, the sword! It's magnificent!

**Lady**  (*very seriously*) Think carefully what you say. The scabbard is worth ten swords, for while you wear it you shall lose no blood, however badly you are wounded. Have good care of it, and beware the evil woman who will try to steal it from you. Never be parted from it. Farewell!

*The Lady of the Lake disappears into the mist.*

**Arthur**  *(bewildered)* She has vanished. What magic have I witnessed?

**Merlin**  Greater magic than mine. She can weave spells of enchantment, and she will protect you when I am no longer with you. But that lies in the future. The present is for merriment! To Camelot!

# SCENE FOUR

*The banqueting hall at Camelot*

**Narrator** *So King Arthur and Merlin return to Camelot amid great rejoicing, for his knights had feared that Arthur was dead. That evening there is a great feast.*

**Arthur** *(passing his sword round the table)* Behold the fine blade, how it glints in the firelight. Witness the rich jewels at its hilt!

**Gryflet** *(kissing the sword and passing it on)* May it serve you well, noble lord.

*Knocking at the hall door. Sir Pellinore enters and kneels at Arthur's feet.*

**Pellinore** Sire, I beg leave to join your court, and to ask your forgiveness for the grievous wrongs I did you.

**Arthur**  Merlin has already spoken for you. You are welcome to join our fellowship. I know to my cost that you are a strong and valiant fighter! Our wounds are healed – let our quarrel be healed too. *(Sternly)* But first you must make peace with good Sir Gryflet, whose master lies dead in his grave.

**Gryflet**  I will forgive you. Come, clasp hands.

*Sir Pellinore and Sir Gryflet clasp hands. Everyone cheers.*

**Arthur**  Merlin, it is as you foretold. This day Sir Pellinore becomes a noble knight of my court!

**Merlin**  Indeed, a place waits for him at the table. On each seat you will find a name in letters of gold. Each knight will come at the time appointed. When a knight dies, his name will fade from his seat. But the memory of the Knights of the Round Table shall live for evermore. Many strange adventures will begin here as you sit at the table.

**Arthur** *(solemnly)* All of you who sit here with me, let us make an oath together. Let this be the first day of the Round Table. Do no murder nor any cruel or wicked thing. Save damsels in distress, give mercy to those who ask it, and keep to the truth. Swear!

**Everyone** *(loudly)* We swear! Long live King Arthur!

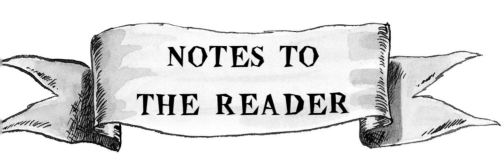

# NOTES TO THE READER

Did Arthur really exist? No one knows for sure. And did he really die? Or does he lie with his knights in a deep sleep underground, waiting to come to our rescue again in a time of crisis, as legend tells us?

In *Excalibur* we learn how King Arthur receives his famous sword from the Lady of the Lake, and swears to use it wisely and well. It also shows the setting up of that famous brotherhood – the Knights of the Round Table.

## Arthur

Arthur is one of the great British folk heroes – chivalrous, honest and loyal.

## Merlin

Merlin is a mix of prophet, wizard and advisor. He is able to appear from nowhere to help Arthur.

## Morgan le Fay

Arthur's half-sister is a wicked enchantress. When Arthur receives Excalibur he is warned against her.

## Camelot and Avalon

Camelot is most likely a legendary version of Cadbury castle, near Glastonbury in Somerset. Avalon, the 'other world', is also thought to be near Glastonbury. Long ago, the plain around Glastonbury Tor was covered by water, which was perhaps the origin of Lake Avalon.

# READY, STEADY, ACT!

Now that you have read this play, it's time to perform it for an audience. This will be quite a challenge, as you will need to create a magical atmosphere…

## CHOOSING THE PARTS

Choose who will play each part. Hold an audition for the six roles.

- The Narrator is a clear speaker who talks directly to the audience.
- Merlin is a wizard of power and mystery.
- King Arthur is brave and noble, but hot-headed.
- Gryflet is a young squire, keen to avenge his dead master.
- The Lady of the Lake is beautiful and strange, like a mysterious dream.
- Sir Pellinore is a bold and dangerous knight, who later becomes a good friend.
- The three robbers can be played by members of the cast in hoods.

Choose lines from each character and see who says them best.

## SETTING THE SCENE

It would be really tricky to show the castle, the lake, the hall and the forest with real scenery. Perhaps use one or two well-positioned props or banners.

# WHAT YOU WILL NEED

## Costumes

Unless you are lucky enough to have access to realistic costumes, you will have to improvise. A simple way would be to all dress in black and add cloaks and swords, false beards or face paints. The Lady wears a white dress and golden girdle. Find her some floaty fabric to trail behind her for a cloak.

Can you make some armour? Or at least some helmets? You could use the pictures in the book to help.

## Props

Use the text to make a props list. The biggest challenges are the horses and the boat. You might need to mime these scenes, or use sound effects. Could you possibly use bicycles for horses?

## Sound effects and special effects

Can you make the sound of horses' hooves and lapping water? Could you make ripples in a large piece of fabric to suggest the surface of the lake?

How will you convey the magical atmosphere of these myths and legends? Can you find some suitable music – spooky for the lakeside, martial for the fights.

> Did you know...?
> The word 'Avalon' comes from a Celtic word, meaning 'apple'.

# SPEAKING AND MOVING

**Speaking**

There are several different styles of speaking in this play. The Narrator knows the story and tells the tale confidently.

Merlin is an immensely wise and powerful wizard. How will this show in his voice?

Sir Pellinore changes from boastful to humble during the play, and this is clear from the way he speaks.

**Moving**

In the first scene Sir Gryflet re-enters wounded. How do you think he will move? Remember, he may be in pain, but he still needs to be able to deliver his lines.

The various fights will need careful staging to be effective but safe. Practise doing them in slow motion.

The Lady of the Lake moves as if she is floating – slowly, quietly and smoothly.

**What next?**

Now you have acted this play, you might want to:

- Write some spells for Merlin – can you make them rhyme?
- Design a beautiful costume for the Lady of the Lake, or for one of the knights.